First published 2003 by Contender Books
Contender Books is a division of
The Contender Entertainment Group
48 Margaret Street
London W1W 8SE
www.contendergroup.com/books

**For more Tractor Tom fun and games, log on to his website
http://www.tractortom.com**

This edition published 2003
1 3 5 7 9 10 8 6 4 2

Great Ormond Street Hospital Children's Charity.
Registered charity no. 235825.
The Contender Entertainment Group will give 5p from the sale of this
Tractor Tom product to Great Ormond Street Hospital Children's Charity.

ISBN 1 84357 075 0

Text by Rebecca Gee
Designed by BURVILLE RILEY
Production by Kate Gribble
Printed in Italy

TRACTOR TOM
ANNUAL
2004

CONTENTS

'TOM-TOM, TOM-TOM!'

Tom is saying 'hello!' to you! He's really pleased to meet you! Our favourite shiny red tractor wants you to have lots of fun reading stories all about him and his friends on Springhill Farm. He's also got lots of games, puzzles and activities for you to do and he can't wait for you to start! Turn over and explore the exciting world of Tractor Tom and his friends...

INTRODUCTION

Tractor Tom

Brave, resourceful Tractor Tom – he always saves the day! What would we do without him?

Farmer Fi

Kind and caring, she works hard on Springhill Farm all year long and looks after everyone on the farm.

Farmhand Matt

Helps Fi out with all the jobs she has to do and is full of great ideas – some of which turn out to be not so great!

Rev

A big, strong and shiny pick-up truck, Rev's engine has a very loud roar!

Buzz

Young, zippy and fun, and a bit of a troublemaker!

Riff

Sensible Riff is the most organised of them all. She tidies up everything!

Mo
Mo is a gentle, friendly cow. She gives Fi her milk every morning.

Purdey
A sleepy, fussy cat, who likes her cream and likes her naps.

Wack and Bach
The Springhill Farm ducks – they are a little crazy!

Wheezy
A little older than the others, Wheezy likes to take things slow – until harvest time that is!

The Sheep
Mad, mischievous and always making mayhem! Who knows what they'll get up to next?

Winnie
Beautiful Winnie can be scatty and sometimes forgets to keep an eye on her foal, Snicker!

Snicker
Another naughty youngster, Snicker just loves causing trouble with his best mate Buzz.

9

MEET TRACTOR TOM!

Tom is our hero! He is a bright red tractor, and he is very strong and tough. Fi and Matt think he is really helpful as he works so hard on Springhill Farm. He is always having great ideas to solve problems on the farm, but he likes having lots of fun too! Tom is always trying to help out his friends and he cheers them up when they are sad. This makes everyone on the farm love him very much.

Tractor Tom – what would we do without you?

What makes Tom go?

Tractors have lots of different parts to make them work. Can you find all these on the picture of Tractor Tom here?

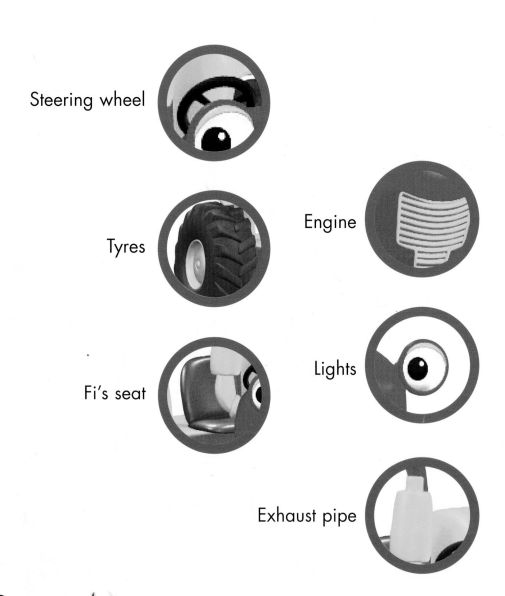

Steering wheel

Tyres

Engine

Fi's seat

Lights

Exhaust pipe

Did you know?

Some tractors are so big that their back tyres are even taller than the farmer! Tom's tyres aren't as big as Fi though.

A tractor pulls its PLOUGH through the soil to turn it over and make it ready to plant seeds.

Tractors use a MOWER attachment to cut fields of long grass. Farmers leave the grass to dry out to make hay.

Just like most tractors, Tom has a TRAILER which he uses to transport heavy loads to and from the farm.

A SURPRISE CARNIVAL FOR FI

It was a cloudy day at Springhill Farm. Tom and Fi had been invited to take part in the Beckton Carnival, but they had to pick all the carrots before it rained, or they would be ruined. Tom and Fi were really disappointed, but Fi said 'I know Matt, you and Rev can go instead of us!'

Matt knew Fi and Tom really wanted to go to the carnival. 'I've got a great idea!' he whispered to Tom. 'Why don't we have our own carnival here?'

'Tom-tom, tom-tom,' said Tom – he was really excited. Matt asked Tom to keep Fi away from the farm all day while he got everything organised.

While Tom and Fi went to pick the carrots, Matt got everyone together to organise the Springhill Farm Carnival. 'Are you ready to party?' he shouted.

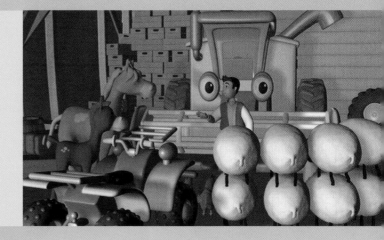

Fi had started to pick carrots, but Tom was being really slow. 'Come on Tom, we haven't got all day,' moaned Fi.

Back at the farm, all the animals were practising the jobs Matt had given them. The hens put on their dancing costumes, Winnie and Snicker tried out their tapdancing, and Riff tried to organise the sheep into doing something useful. 'Are you sure about this, Riff?' asked Matt, worriedly.

Tom and Fi finally finished picking carrots. 'At last! Now we can go back to the farm and have a nice cold drink!' said Fi. Oh no! Tom knew Matt wouldn't be ready with Fi's surprise yet, so he had to think of a way to keep her busy for a little while longer. 'Tom!' sighed Fi. 'We've been all over the farm, checked all the gates are closed, and tidied up all the fields. Now, can we PLEASE get back to the farmyard?!' she begged.

Buzz was keeping lookout. When he saw Tom and Fi making their way home, he rushed into the barn to warn Matt. 'OK, now hide everyone!' whispered Matt. 'Remember, this is supposed to be a surprise!' Matt shut the barn door and waited outside for Fi and Tom.

Fi was surprised to see him. 'What are you doing here?' she asked. 'I thought you were going to the carnival?'

'There's been a change of plan,' explained Matt. 'You couldn't go to the Beckton Carnival, so we've brought our own carnival to you! Everyone's going to join in!'

'That's amazing – thanks Matt!' said Fi happily. 'You knew about this, didn't you Tom? That's why you've been so slow all day. What would we do without you?'

Matt grabbed Fi's hand. 'Come on Fi, it's time to turn you into the Carnival Queen!' Fi sat in Tom's trailer and Matt put a crown made of carrots on her head. Matt decided to be the announcer.

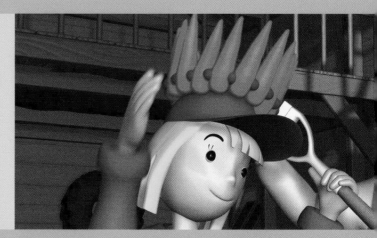

'Welcome to the Springhill Farm Carnival,' he shouted. Everyone started to come out of the barn in a long trail. 'Meet our amazing samba dancing hens, riding on Rev!' The hens shook their tail feathers to the sound of the music.

'On cowbells, the one and only, Musical Mo!' Mo came out of the barn waving her head and tail proudly, to make her bells ring beautifully.

'Now welcome those two tapdancing hoofers, Winnie and Snicker!' The horses clicked their heels and jumped in perfect time to each other. Fi could tell they had been practising all day.

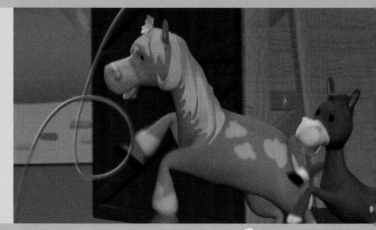

'Please wave to the carnival princess, Purdey, on her royal buggy, Buzz!' Purdey raised her head and smiled to everyone as if she was a real princess.

'Sway to the beat of Wack and Bach on the steel drum!' The ducks, riding on top of Wheezy, jumped up and down on a metal dustbin lid to make some really tuneful sounds that surprised everyone. 'And what's Wheezy spraying? Clouds of colourful confetti!'

'And who's this? Riff at the head of the sheep marching band!' Riff twirled her cane as she led out the sheep, who were playing a lovely carnival tune on their horns.

'Finally, a very big hand for the stars of the carnival – Queen Fi and Tractor Tom!' Fi was so happy, she called to Matt, 'It's the best carnival we've ever been to! Let's all do it again next year!'

CARNIVAL DAY!

Colour this picture of Fi's special carnival and make it as bright as you can. Why don't you add some glitter to really make the party sparkle?

17

MEET FI AND MATT!

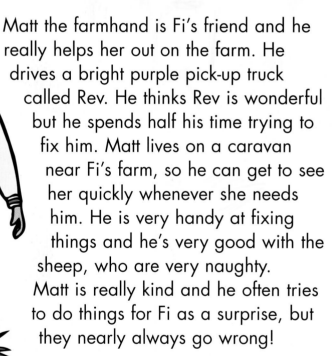

Springhill Farm belongs to Farmer Fi. She lives in a farmhouse in the farmyard with Purdey and Riff, her cat and dog. Fi loves her farm and everyone who lives there. She looks after them all, but she couldn't do it without the help of Tom and Matt. She is very kind and sensible and knows what to do when things go wrong. She can be a bit bossy though, just like a teacher or a mummy!

Matt the farmhand is Fi's friend and he really helps her out on the farm. He drives a bright purple pick-up truck called Rev. He thinks Rev is wonderful but he spends half his time trying to fix him. Matt lives on a caravan near Fi's farm, so he can get to see her quickly whenever she needs him. He is very handy at fixing things and he's very good with the sheep, who are very naughty. Matt is really kind and he often tries to do things for Fi as a surprise, but they nearly always go wrong!

Fi's jobs

As you can see from these five pictures of Fi, she is always busy on the farm with all the jobs she has to do. Try to match up Fi and her tools with the jobs waiting for her on the opposite page.

Did you know?

Farmers have to get up really early every morning to start their work on the farm – usually before it is light.

Farmers have to be very strong and fit, as they have to be able to lift heavy loads up and down, and chase naughty animals when they won't do as they are told! Fi drinks Mo's milk to make her strong.

Farmers can't stop their work at the weekends or at Christmas, as the cows need to be milked every day, and the animals need to be given their food. If farmers want to have a break or a holiday, they need to ask someone to look after their farm for them. Fi is lucky because Matt can help her out when she needs him to.

Farmers sell some of the things they produce on the farm to supermarkets, like milk, eggs, meat, fruit and vegetables. Farmers also have their own special markets to sell their animals or the food that they grow. Fi grows carrots and apples on her farm, and later in this book you can read a story about Matt taking Fi's apples to the market.

DOWN ON THE FARM

Do you live in a town with lots of houses and shops? Perhaps you live in the countryside with narrow lanes and fields? If you visit the countryside you will probably see different kinds of farms.

A farm is where animals like cows and pigs and sheep live, or plants like wheat, barley or vegetables grow. All these are needed to make the food that we buy in the shops. Butter, cheese and yoghurt come from cow's milk. Ham and bacon come from pigs and wool and meat from sheep. Bread is made from wheat flour.

People who work on farms are called farmers, like Fi. A farmer needs a tractor like Tractor Tom to help with all the jobs that need doing around the farm.

Sometimes people spend their holidays on a farm and can help look after the animals. You will have to get up very early if you want to see the cows being milked. Always remember to shut the big gates around the farm so the animals don't get out.

There are lots of things to hear and smell and see on a farm. Near the farmhouse where the farmer lives you might hear chickens or ducks or geese. They run around making a lot of noise. The cowsheds where the cows live in winter can be smelly. Sometimes farmers grow whole fields of plants with bright yellow flowers. They are used to make food for the sheep to eat in winter or to make a special oil from their seeds.

Can you point to some of the things you see on a farm in this picture? Put a tick in each box when you have found them.

- a farmhouse
- barn
- hen house
- food troughs
- Tractor Tom
- Wheezy the combine harvester
- gates
- hedges
- Fi the farmer
- Matt the farmhand
- Mo the cow
- sheep
- Purdey the cat
- Riff the dog
- Winnie and Snicker

OUT FOR A WALK

Tom and Fi love going out into the fields to work. They like being surrounded by the countryside and they enjoy the smell of the grass and the flowers in the hedges, the buzz of the bees and the sounds of the birds. They are really lucky to live in the countryside all the time, but you don't have to live in the country to see and hear these things – you can even find them in the garden or a park!

It would be fun to collect some things to remind you of a walk in the countryside, park or garden. You could stick them in a book or draw pictures of what you saw. The book could be your own Nature Scrap Book. You could show your book to your friends.

Here are some things to look for. You will probably have lots more ideas of your own.

Collect:
- **a leaf**
- **a feather**
- **a piece of wood**
- **an empty snail shell**
- **a daisy flower to press flat**
- **a shiny stone**
- **a fluffy grass head**
- **some moss**

Draw pictures of what you see under a log or stone, the shape of the clouds in the sky, a tree, a flower too big to press, an animal footprint.

RHYME TIME!

One day I saw a big blue cow
Raise her head and chew
I said, 'Good morning, Mrs Cow,'
But all she said was 'Moo!'

One day I saw a woolly lamb
I followed it quite far,
I said 'Good morning, little lamb,'
But all it said was 'Baa!'

One day I saw a dappled horse
Cropping in the hay,
I said 'Good morning, Mrs Horse,'
But all she said was 'Neigh!'

24

Baa, baa, black sheep,
Have you any wool?
Yes sir, yes sir,
Three bags full;
One for the master,
And one for the dame,
And one for the little boy
Who lives down the lane.

The big brown hen
   and Mrs Duck
Went walking out together;
They talked about all sorts
   of things –
The farmyard, and the weather.
But all I heard was 'Cluck!
   Cluck! Cluck!'
And 'Quack! Quack! Quack!'
   from Mrs Duck.

Hey diddle diddle
The cat and the fiddle,
The cow jumped over the moon;
The little dog laughed
To see such fun,
And the dish ran away
With the spoon.

MEET THE SHEEP!

The sheep get everywhere on Springhill Farm! Fi thinks there are about seven, but they get up to such mischief it's hard to tell! Matt thinks they are 'a bunch of woolly hooligans'. They are not like ordinary sheep, and they never do as they are told. They love learning silly tricks and games, and they have been known to sunbathe and paint – once they even had a disco after Fi taught them to dance! Tom and Fi have given up trying to control the sheep, and they usually leave that job to poor old Riff. Her barking makes them get together and behave themselves – for a while, at least!

Did you know?

Wool usually comes from sheep, but you can get wool from goats, llamas and camels. The best wool comes from lambs.

Wool is great for making jumpers because it's warm, keeps out water and doesn't crease. You can also use it for making blankets and carpets.

Farmers shear their sheep in early summer. Can you imagine Fi trying to catch her sheep to give them a haircut?!

Every summer farmers also give their sheep a bath in special liquid to kill all the bugs that live in their wool. Fi must find this very difficult too!

Incredible dancing sheep!

Why don't you make your own dancing sheep? It's really easy to do and great fun!

You will need:

- **A long piece of newspaper**
- **Glue**
- **Scissors**
- **Cotton wool**
- **Black felt tip pen**

Take your piece of newspaper and fold it like a fan – a grown up will show you how to do this if you find it quite hard. The width of each fold should be about seven centimetres. You need to fold the paper 12 or 14 times if you can, so you 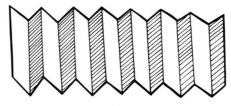 make lots of dancing sheep. On the top fold of the fan, use the template to the right to draw the outline of the sheep against the folded edge. It might not look like a sheep yet – but it soon will! Now cut round the outline and unfold your newspaper until it's flat – can you see the dancing sheep now? They are all holding hands! Make them look more like sheep by sticking cotton wool on their bodies, and use your pen to draw some eyes and a mouth on their faces. Now, hold on to both ends of your newspaper sheep and make them dance!

PAINTING DAY

One morning on Springhill Farm, while Fi was out in the fields working with Tom, Matt had a brilliant idea.

'Can you keep a secret?' he asked the hens. 'I'm going to paint Fi's house, but I want it to be a surprise.' The hens clucked excitedly in reply, and Matt started getting everything ready for the big job ahead.

Just then, Buzz came roaring into the farmyard. He was having a very boring morning indeed. Fi didn't have any jobs for him to do that day, so he was having fun on his own – racing around Springhill Farm and pretending he was big strong truck like Rev.

'Vroom, vroom!' squealed Buzz eagerly, rushing around the yard as fast as he could. Oh no! He's crashed into Matt's paint cans!

Matt was very angry. 'The paint's gone everywhere!' he shouted.

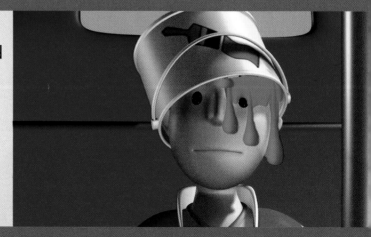

Buzz raced off, leaving the mess behind him. Matt sighed in disappointment. It was going to take him ages to clear up – and he hadn't even started painting the house yet!

Out in the fields, Buzz bumped into Snicker. They had a great time gallivanting about the field together. All too soon, however, they grew bored of their games and raced off to find something else to play with.

Back at the farmhouse, Matt had finally cleared up the mess that Buzz had made. He looked around the tidy farmyard, smiling in satisfaction, and then climbed his ladder to start painting Fi's house.

Just as he got his paintbrush out, Buzz and Snicker came into the yard. They saw the paint pots and decided they would make great playthings! They grabbed as many as they could and rushed out of the yard, knocking Matt off his ladder on the way.

'Oh no! Not again!' cried Matt as he looked at the messy yard. There was paint spilt everywhere for the second time! As Buzz and Snicker hurried away from the farm, they didn't notice they were spilling paint all over the road. Matt decided to follow the paint trail to catch the naughty pair.

'You two!' Matt shouted sternly, as Buzz and Snicker scampered away. 'Come back here! You've got to help clear up all this mess you've made. Hey!' Matt chased Buzz and Snicker all over the farm.

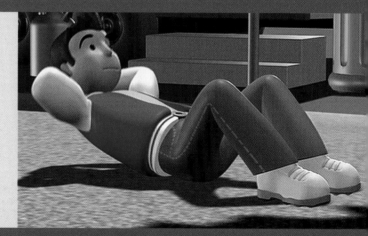

All the other animals watched the chase with building excitement. They thought it looked like great fun and decided to join in – but they knocked Matt flying. 'Ow! My ankle!' he cried.

Meanwhile, Tom came chugging into the farmyard after his hard day's work. He couldn't believe his eyes! All the animals were rolling in the paint and Matt was nowhere to be found. It was absolute chaos!

Before Tom could do anything, Buzz and Snicker arrived. They led him to Matt, who was still rubbing his ankle. 'Thank you Tom,' he said as Tom lifted him up. 'But what am I going to do about the messy yard? Please will you take me back before Fi sees it?'

But just then, Fi came round the corner. She took a concerned look at Matt's ankle and decided he needed a bandage. 'Let's take you back to the farmyard,' she said. Oh no! Matt didn't want her to see the mess, but it was too late.

But Snicker and Buzz knew they had been really naughty, so they decided to do something to help. They asked Riff to round up the animals, and they turned Wheezy into a cleaning-up machine. Wheezy swept round the yard as quickly as he could, and finished just in time.

'Matt! You've cleaned up the yard!' said Fi. 'It looks great.'

'Erm… did I?' asked Matt, looking puzzled. 'Is this anything to do with you two?' he asked Buzz and Snicker. 'I suppose you're not as much trouble as we always think you are.'

Then Matt looked sad. He still hadn't painted Fi's house, and where were all the paint pots now?

Matt told Fi all about his horrid day. 'The funny thing is,' he said, 'I still don't know where those paint pots are. I'm really sorry Fi.'

'Oh no! I think I know exactly what has happened to that paint!' she laughed. 'Look at those naughty sheep!'

They looked at the sheep, who were busy rolling the paint all over the grass. Matt and Fi groaned. 'It looks like we haven't finished tidying up after all!' they said.

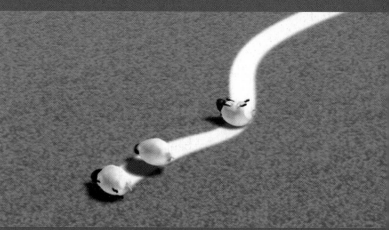

CAN YOU GUESS WHAT THE SHEEP WERE PAINTING? SEE PAGE 62 TO FIND OUT!

HELP MATT!

Poor Matt! He really wanted to give Fi a nice surprise, but his day was so busy he didn't get a chance to paint Fi's house. Can you help him by colouring in the house for him? What colour do you think Fi would choose? And why don't you make her flowers bright and cheerful to make the house look even better?

FOLLOW THOSE FEET!

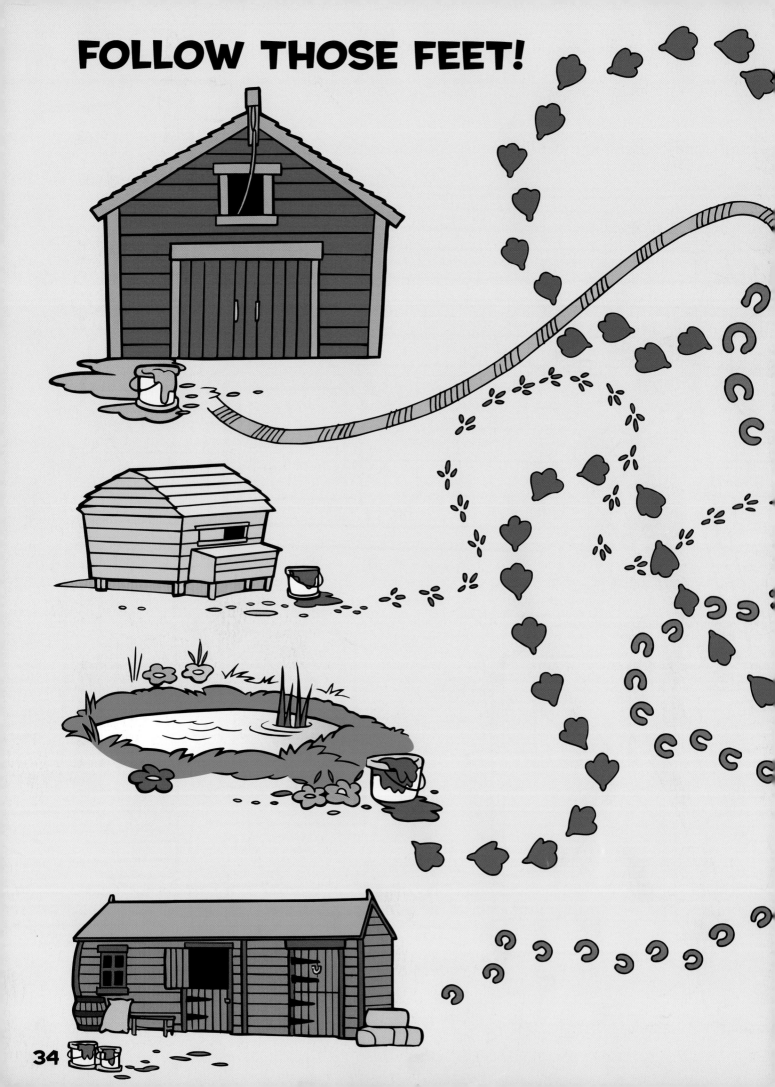

What a mess! Tom's naughty friends have walked through Matt's paint and have spread it all over the farm! Can you follow the paths to find out whose footprints are whose?

MEET PURDEY AND RIFF!

Purdey

Purdey is a ginger and white cat, and like most cats she is very lazy. You can usually find her curled up asleep in warm, quiet places. She can sleep anywhere – even in the middle of a race! Purdey is a clever cat, but she likes to get everyone else to do things for her. She always arrives just as the work is done and the food is ready – but sometimes she drives Fi mad as she can be the fussiest cat in the world!

Riff

Riff is Fi's sheepdog. Fi gets on very well with Riff because they are so alike. Riff can be really bossy and likes to sort everyone out. Riff's best friend on the farm is Tom, and they often work together when Fi is having trouble with the naughty sheep. Riff can always round them up with her loud bark!

Purdey isn't awake very often, but she is today!
Here are six pictures of Purdey – but only two are the same. Can you spot which two and draw a circle round them?

MEET WACK AND BACH AND THE HENS!

Wack and Bach

Wack and Bach are Springhill Farm's lovely white ducks. They live on the pond in the farmyard. They aren't very clever and are always getting in the way – they are never very far away as they are so silly they have forgotten that they can fly!

The hens

The fat brown hens live in the farmyard and give Fi lovely eggs for breakfast every morning. They are quite nosy and whenever they get the chance they try to join in with Tom's work. They do try to be helpful – and Matt thinks their beaks are very useful whenever he needs a hammer!

Egg-citing eggs!

Some people like to eat boiled eggs for breakfast and dip bread soldiers into the yummy yolk. Have you ever tried one? Hard-boiled eggs are also very tasty and very good for you, and it is fun to peel the shell off the outside before you eat them. Some people think they are a bit boring, so why don't you make them look more interesting? Ask a grown up to cook you some hardboiled eggs, and then decorate them. Here are some ideas to get you started… the trouble is they will look too good to eat!

Did you know?

Most of the eggs we eat come from hens, but you can also eat eggs from ducks and some other birds.

Eggs are really good for you. You can eat them on their own in lots of different ways. How do you like to eat your eggs?

Most eggs that you find in supermarkets come from hens who live in cages or barns – but some hens wander around outside and only come indoors to lay their eggs. These are called FREE RANGE. Fi's hens are free range – they get everywhere!

Eggs have to be collected by the farmer straight away, as they are only about two or three days old when they are sold in the supermarket. No wonder Fi is always busy!

Each person in this country eats about 170 eggs in a year – that's a lot of eggs – but the best hens can lay 300 eggs a year!

It is a busy day on Springhill Farm and Fi has asked Tractor Tom to do some counting for her. She needs to know how many of each thing she has on the farm. Can you help Tom find everything?

Put a circle round each item as you find it, and write the number in the correct box.

Buzz

Wack and Bach

Hens

Hay bales

Birds in the sky

Eggs

Sheep

Trees in the field

Flowers

Apples in the trees

A YEAR ON SPRINGHILL FARM

Fi has different jobs to do during the year. This is because the weather changes through the four times called seasons. These seasons are spring, summer, autumn and winter. **What season is it now?**

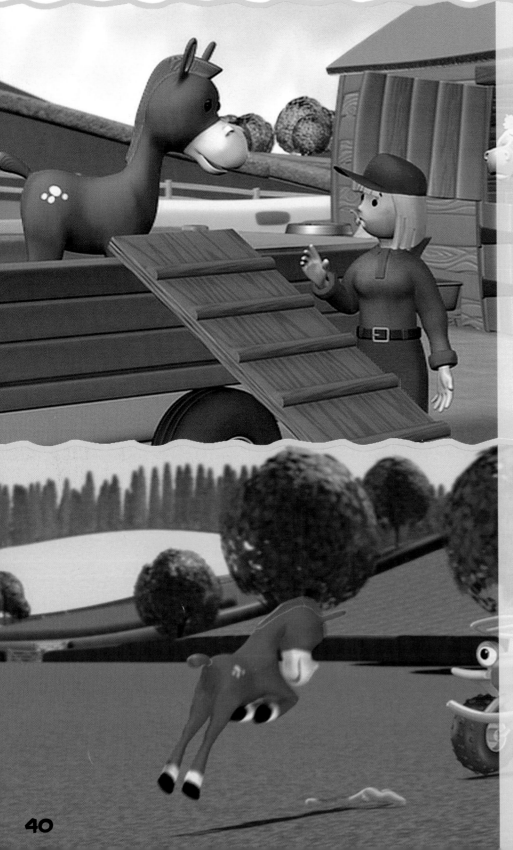

In January, the first month of the year, it is winter. It is cold and the days are short. Animals live in sheds and stables. Fi has to feed them hay and silage as there is not enough grass growing in the fields. Silage is cut grass which is stored in a special way so that it stays sweet and fresh. In the winter a few vegetables like cabbages and carrots will grow.

In spring the days get longer and the sun begins to shine. Baby animals like calves, lambs and chicks are born. Tractor Tom and Fi will sow seeds of oats and barley with a machine called a seed drill. Manure or fertiliser is spread on the fields to help the new plants to grow.

All the animals live in the fields in the warm summer. The wheat is collected by Wheezy, the combine harvester. The grass is cut to make winter food for the animals.

During the autumn, when the leaves blow off the trees, Tractor Tom and Fi still have a lot to do. It is time to plough the fields to turn the soil. This makes it ready for growing more seeds next year. Hedges are cut, ditches dug and fences mended to make the farm tidy before the end of the year. Matt helps out with these jobs.

A YEAR ON SPRINGHILL FARM

Seasonal Songs

The north wind doth blow,
And we shall have snow,
And what will poor robin
    do then,
Poor thing?
He'll sit in a barn,
And keep himself warm,
And hide his head under
    his wing.
Poor thing!

The leaves are green
The nuts are brown
They hang so high
They will not come down.

Leave them alone
Till frosty weather
Then they will all
Come down together.

Rain on the green grass,
And rain on the tree,
And rain on the house-top,
But not upon me!

'Brrr! It's a really chilly winter's day!' Fi tells Tom. Add some snowflakes to make it even colder! Poor Fi needs some cosy winter clothes – why don't you make her outfit really bright and cheery to warm her up?

'What strange spring weather we're having today!' says Fi. What happens when it is sunny and rainy at the same time? Can you add something colourful to the sky to show Fi? She's getting a bit wet. Can you give her an umbrella to keep her dry?

'Phew! This is the hottest summer's day I can ever remember!' Fi says to Tom. What is missing from the sky? Can you draw it in?

'Look Tom, it's so windy all the leaves are falling off the trees!' says Fi. 'Tom-tom, tom-tom!' – Tom says autumn is his favourite time of year. He has lots of work to do and is always busy. Can you give him some hay bales to take back to the farm? And Fi needs a snug jumper and a pair of gloves to keep her warm. Look at the sky. Do you think it is going to rain?

Seasonal Songs

In August, when the days
    are hot,
I like to find a shady spot,
And hardly move a single
    bit –
And sit –
And sit –
And sit –
And sit!

A little bit of blowing,
A little bit of snow,
A little bit of growing,
And crocuses will show;
On every twig that's lonely
A new green leaf will
    spring;
On every patient tree-top
A thrush will stop and sing.

MEET MO, WINNIE AND SNICKER!

Mo

Mo is Fi's big milk cow. She is friendly, kind and always smiling. She has a very important job on Springhill Farm – she provides the milk for Fi's breakfast, Purdey's morning snack and Fi's bedtime cocoa! Mo loves to watch everyone rushing around the farm – even when they get into trouble! But she doesn't really join in all the mischief. She just smiles, moos and gets on with her favourite hobby – eating grass!

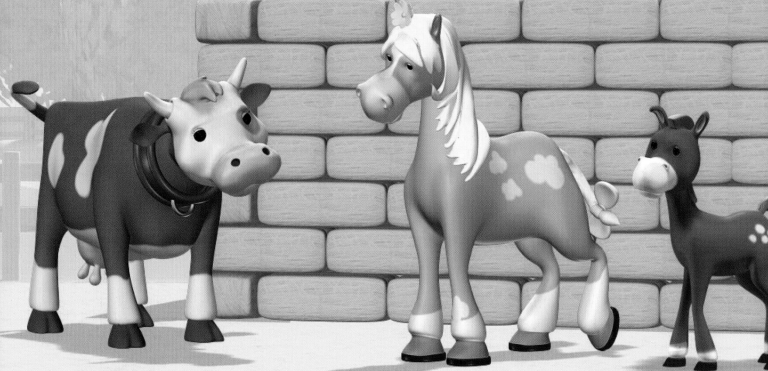

Winnie

Winnie is a lovely gentle horse. She always likes to look as beautiful as she can. She has a long blonde mane, and she likes to wear a flower behind her ear. She may be lovely, but she wants to get her own way! If she doesn't want to do something, she won't!

Snicker

Snicker is Winnie's foal. He is like Winnie – he likes to do things his way! But he is only little and keeps getting into trouble. His best friend on the farm is Buzz. They are both fed up with being told what to do, and together they can cause all sorts of mischief on Springhill Farm! Good old Tractor Tom usually has to sort it out!

Giddy up!

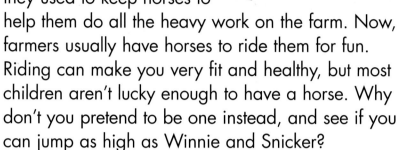

A long time ago, farmers didn't have tractors like Tom and they used to keep horses to help them do all the heavy work on the farm. Now, farmers usually have horses to ride them for fun. Riding can make you very fit and healthy, but most children aren't lucky enough to have a horse. Why don't you pretend to be one instead, and see if you can jump as high as Winnie and Snicker?

First you'll need some horsey ears!
You will need:

- **A piece of card or thick paper**
- **Scissors**
- **Pens or paint**
- **Sellotape**

Use the templates below as a guide for drawing the ear shapes on to your card. Now ask a grown up to help you cut round the outline. Paint the ears whatever colour you like – you could even add a flower like Winnie's! Now cut out a long strip of card which will stretch all the way around your head – you may need some help with this! Attach the painted ears to the strip of card and then fasten the band around your head, to make a horsey crown.

Now you are ready! One… two… three… gallop and… jump! Ask a grown up to measure how high you can jump, and see if you can beat them. Don't forget to neigh just like a real horse!

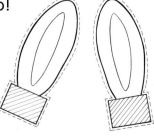

Did you know?

Cows don't always live in fields. They only stay outside in the summer, when the grass is long and they can eat it all day. In the winter, cows live in the farmyard in barns and eat hay or silage that machines like Tom and Wheezy have collected for them.

Milk from cows is very good for us. Milk has something called CALCIUM in it – this helps our bones to grow big and strong – that is why Fi has Mo's milk on her cereal every morning!

Usually we get milk from cows, but you can buy milk from other animals like goats and sheep. Some people are allergic to milk so they have to drink a different kind of milk called SOY milk. This is made from plants. Have you ever tried milk from other animals?

Milk is also used to make all sorts of other foods, like butter, cheese, cream or yoghurt. What is your favourite food made from milk?

Farmers have to milk their cows two or three times a day – it's lucky Fi has only got one cow or she would be too busy to do any other work on the farm!

MEET WHEEZY, BUZZ AND REV!

Wheezy

Wheezy is Fi's combine harvester and he lives in the barn. He is quite old now, and is very wise and clever. He is always trying to tell everyone stories about the old days, but usually they are too busy to listen, so poor old Wheezy quite often feels sad and a bit useless. Tractor Tom is very good at cheering him up! Wheezy's most important job is to bring in the wheat and hay in the autumn, and everyone laughs when they watch him coughing his way through the fields!

Buzz

Buzz is a bright blue quad-bike. He's very fast and can take Fi or Matt round the farm very quickly – but he can't do all the jobs that Tom can do, and that makes him very cross. Sometimes he thinks he will try anyway, which always leads to big trouble...

Rev

Rev is Matt's pick-up truck. He is bright purple with a loud horn and a huge engine. He's always showing off as he is faster and stronger than anyone else on the farm. But Matt is very proud of him as he is very helpful and takes Matt everywhere he needs to go.

What's my job?

Tom, Rev, Wheezy and Buzz are all machines on Springhill Farm, and they all have different jobs to do. Why don't you match up who would be best at all the different jobs below? Don't forget, some of the friends could do more than one thing!

The hay bales need to be taken back to the farm

Matt needs to take Riff to the vet

Fi needs to find the sheep all over the farm

Purdey needs to be helped out of the tree

The wheat field needs cutting

The apples need to be taken to market

Did you know?

Combine harvesters are large farming machines that are even taller than tractors. Their job is to cut the plant once it is ready for harvesting. They move across each field, separating the seed from the stem and cleaning the grain as they work. Combine harvesters then store the grain inside themselves until it is ready to be collected by a tractor. This is why Tractor Tom and Wheezy make such a good team!

Combine harvesters also collect cereals like wheat, oats and barley.

Wheat is used to make flour. We need flour to cook cakes, bread and pizzas.

Oats make a good breakfast cereal.

Barley is used to brew beer and can also be used for making all sorts of foods. It can be eaten on its own like pasta, combined with meat to make hamburgers and also used as an ingredient in things like soups and stews.

APPLE SQUASH

It was a lovely autumn morning on Springhill Farm, but Wheezy was feeling sorry for himself. He had finished harvesting the wheat but was now back in the barn with nothing to do – and he felt useless.

Over in the farmhouse, Fi was having trouble with Purdey because, like a lot of cats, she was a very fussy eater.

'What's the matter, Purdey?' asked Fi. 'You've always liked this cat food until now.'

'Miaow!' said Purdey, shaking her head. She didn't even want a saucer of milk.

Fi went to meet Matt in the orchard, as they had a lot of apples to pick.

'There are so many apples this year, we'd better get started!' said Matt. Soon they had filled lots of boxes in Tom's trailer, and were ready for a rest.

'I'm going to try and feed Purdey again,' Fi said.

Back in the farmhouse, Fi offered Purdey some lovely kippers and some tasty sardines but still Purdey shook her head. 'You really are a fusspot!' moaned Fi.

'Miaow!' agreed Purdey.

Tom went to see Wheezy. He was still bored and fed up. Tom wished he could think of something to keep the old combine harvester busy, but just then Fi called Tom to take her back to the orchard.

Matt and Fi spent all day picking apples and putting them in Tom and Rev, but there were still plenty more left on the trees. 'I hope we can sell them all!' said Matt. 'I'll take some to the market and see if anyone wants to buy them, but there are so many I can't take them all. Tom can put the rest in the barn for now.'

Tom unloaded all his boxes of apples in the barn. There were so many he even had to put some on Wheezy, who was fast asleep and snoring loudly. He woke up and jumped in surprise. Uh-oh! He squashed lots of apples by accident, and soon the barn was covered in sticky apple juice.

Just then, Matt came back from the market. 'All the farmers have got loads of apples this year, just like us,' he called to Fi. 'So there's no point in taking any more.'

'Oh no! What are we going to do with all our apples then?' asked Fi.

'I don't know,' sighed Matt.

Fi was really fed up. She went back to the farmhouse to try yet again to feed Purdey, but the naughty cat even refused a bowl of cream – usually her favourite.

Tom had an idea, but he needed Matt's help. He asked Matt to come into the barn so he could show him something.

'Oh dear! What a mess!' cried Matt, treading in the big puddle of apple juice that Wheezy had made.

'Tom-tom, tom-tom,' said Tom, as he explained his great idea to Matt.

'Hey! Let's give it a try!' said Matt.

Matt called everyone except Fi into the barn to help, and soon all the animals were busy fetching, sawing and hammering with Matt and Tom.

Rev kept watch outside the barn to keep Tom's idea secret from Fi, but Fi could hear all the noise and came to see what was happening.

'Come on Rev,' said Fi, 'I want to know what's going on in that barn.'

'It's okay Fi,' called Matt, 'we've finished – you can come in now.'

'Presenting the Wheezy Special Apple Juice Making Machine!' announced Matt, as Fi came into the barn. She couldn't believe her eyes! Tom had found a new job for poor old Wheezy, and he was now busy squashing all the apples and turning them into delicious fresh apple juice.

'That's brilliant!' cried Fi. 'Now we can use all those apples after all! Well done, Matt.'

'Don't thank me, thank Tom,' said Matt. 'It was all his idea.'

'What would we do without him?' said Fi.

It had turned into a really good day after all, thanks to Tom. Everyone was happy. Wheezy felt useful again, Fi wasn't worried about having too many apples, and Matt went off to market with lots of delicious apple juice.

But best of all – Purdey thought the apple juice was delicious too!

'Oh Purdey,' laughed Fi. 'You really are a funny cat!'

HAYSTACK-SHAPED APPLE MUFFINS!

What a bumper harvest! Even though Wheezy is using most of the apples to make apple squash, Fi takes a few back to the farmhouse to make a delicious treat for everyone – hot apple muffins! Why don't you have a go at making them too? All you need are lots of apples and a grown up to help you!

You will need:

250 g (8 oz) plain flour
1 teaspoon salt
3 teaspoons baking powder
50 g (2 oz) caster sugar
$1/2$ teaspoon ground ginger
$1/2$ teaspoon mixed spice
2 beaten eggs
150 ml (1/4 pint) milk
50 g (2 oz) melted butter
260 g (9 oz) any type of apples

This will make 24 apple muffins.

1. Grease two muffin tins.
2. Peel the apples, cut out the cores and chop the yummy bits of apple into small, bite-sized pieces.
3. Sieve the flour, salt and baking powder into a big bowl and stir in the sugar and the spices. I hope you have an apron on to protect your clothes!
4. In another bowl, mix together the eggs, milk and melted butter. Put this into the flour mixture. Don't worry about it being a bit lumpy – you just need to do this bit as fast as you can!
5. Now put the apples in and mix it all up – quickly, quickly!
6. Get a spoon and put the mixture into the muffin tins. Each little hole should be one-third full, not full right to the top.
7. These now need to go into a hot oven, preheated to 190°C (375°F, Gas Mark 5), for 15–20 minutes. When your apple muffins are cooked they will have grown as tall as haystacks and will be a beautiful golden brown colour.
8. Now you can eat, eat, eat! These are most delicious when they are hot. Why don't you try them with some butter?

Do you think Purdey would like these?

IN THE ORCHARD

Fi, Matt and Tractor Tom are exhausted after their hard day's work picking apples. It's getting dark now, and they are hungry and thirsty. Why don't you help them out?

- Put some more **ROUND** apples in Fi's basket.
- Matt is thirsty. Give him a **SQUARE** carton of juice to drink – don't forget the straw!
- Fi is hungry – give her a **TRIANGLE** shaped ice cream cone to cheer her up.
- Put the **CRESCENT** moon and the **STARS** in the sky.

- Give Tractor Tom some more **OBLONG** crates for his trailer. You can fill them with apples if you like!

MEET... ME!

'Tom-tom, tom-tom!' Tom says now you know all about him and his friends, it's his turn to find out everything about you! Why don't you tell him about yourself?

My name is:

I am _____ years old

Draw your favourite character from *Tractor Tom:*

Draw your favourite food:

Tom lives in the barn with Wheezy and Buzz, Fi lives in the farmhouse with Purdey, and Matt lives in his caravan next to Rev. Tom wants to know who you live with, and what you look like. Why don't you draw a picture of you and all your family to show him? And do you have any pets? Tom would like to know what they look like too.

GOODBYE!

All the hard work on Springhill Farm has been done for this year. Everyone has got a chance to have a big Christmas party before all the jobs start again next year. What are all the friends looking at? Join the dots and find out!

'Tom-tom, tom-tom!' Tom wants to say thank you for all your help – and he can't wait to see you next year!

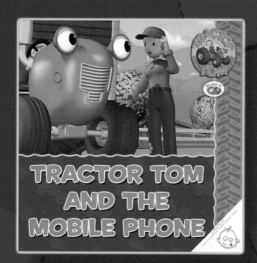
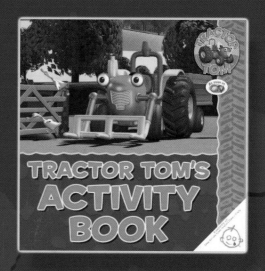
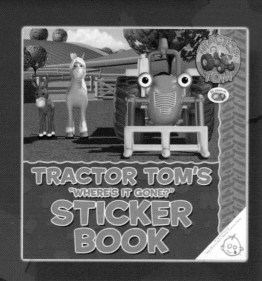

**LOOK OUT FOR TRACTOR TOM TOYS –
OUT THIS YEAR IN ALL GOOD TOYSHOPS!**

SECRET SOLUTIONS

'Tom-tom, tom-tom!' Tom says this is a very special page. Here's where you can find out all the answers to the activities you've been doing throughout the annual. Don't peek unless you've completed them already!

Pages 18 and 19 FI'S JOBS
Fi uses her watering can to give her plants a shower.
Fi gives handfuls of grain to her hungry hens.
Fi sits on her milking stool, with her milking bucket, in order to milk Mo.
Fi uses her big brush to make Winnie and Snicker look beautiful. They get a carrot as a treat too!
Fi and Tom must plough the field.

Page 31 PAINTING SHEEP
Look what those naughty sheep got up to with Matt's paint!

Page 36 MEET PURDEY AND RIFF!
This picture was the same.
Did you get it right?

Page 38 and 39 COUNT WITH TOM!
This is the number of items in the picture. Did you spot them all?

• Buzz (1)
• Wack and Bach (2)
• Hens (3)
• Hay bales (4)
• Birds (5, in the sky)
• Eggs (6)
• Sheep (7)
• Trees in the field (8)
• Flowers (9)
• Apples in the trees (10)

Page 46 and 47 WHAT'S MY JOB?
The wheat field needs cutting – roll up Wheezy!
The hay bales need to be taken back to the farm – a job for Tractor Tom.
The apples need to be taken to market – Tom's far too busy on the farm, so Rev helps out here.
Fi needs to find the sheep all over the farm – Buzz is best for this task!
Matt needs to take Riff to the vet – big, comfortable Rev to the rescue.
Purdey needs to be helped out of the tree – another job for Tom, what would we do without him?